MW00620037

BY *Elle Benson*

Elle Benson authored and designed this workbook to help women deepen their sense of self-awareness during pregnancy – an incredible, yet brief, experience. She is a working mother with a passion for leadership and mindfulness.

It is intended to enable pregnant women to engage in activities that facilitate a more personally meaningful pregnancy. Via researched positive psychology tools (like gratitude development and mindfulness training) from UC Berkeley's Greater Good Science Center, you'll cultivate social and emotional well-being during your pregnancy to reduce stress on you, and on your baby. Additionally, these resources can be used postpartum to continue your well-being journey.

Cultivate Your Happiness
Mama-To-Be by Elle Benson

www.CultivateYourHappiness.co

Cover and interior design by
Katemade.co

ISBN: 978-0-578-55345-0

DEDICATED TO

Bellamy Collette Benson

INTRODUCTION

This workbook is intended to help you discover your inner happiness and cultivate joy within your pregnancy. Pregnancy is (luckily!) short-term, so this workbook will help you tune in, with activities and prompts to be in a positive and present mindset. These skills will become vital post-pregnancy, as your world experiences another complete shift.

I started learning mindfulness techniques during my graduate work while studying leadership. Leadership led me into positive psychology, which sparked my interest and passion for happiness development. The lightbulb finally went off when research became evident in reality, as I listened to ten friends in a book club continually say, "I'll be happy when…" I was struck with empathy to think that my incredible, smart, healthy, beautiful friends didn't have the full capacity to own their current happiness. I became obsessed with gathering resources that would ultimately be used to help women cultivate their inner happiness and take ownership of their own self-love journey.

My initial workbook was intended for young professional women – until I got pregnant. I had a healthy pregnancy, but still suffered from the hormonal shifts, public perception and comments about my changing body, stress, and fear about childbirth. My world as I've known it was changing. Would I lose myself once I became a mother? Did I have the capacity to teach resilience, healthy relationships and love?

I was also saddened at a prenatal yoga class to hear my friend talk about her first pregnancy like she didn't even remember it. She was working 14-hour days, and didn't allow herself to fully embrace or acknowledge her pregnancy. So, I prioritized expectant mothers as the intended users of my first workbook. I anticipate future versions for new moms and young professionals.

There is no right or wrong way to utilize this book, no particular order that I recommend or feel would be more beneficial than another. It can be helpful to do some activities with a partner or friend. In other cases, the solitude in completing your workbook will be most enjoyable. The prompts and questions that you find the most challenging might be written just for you, so dig into the prompts that make you the most uncomfortable. Allow this season of life to inspire you and push you.

One thing that mentally helped me cope and connect with my pregnancy was guided meditation. I tried to do thirty-minutes per day. From that experience of turning inward for peace, I finally surrendered to the power of mindfulness. Now that I have a wild toddler, my calm meditation sessions are far from a reality. I have to incorporate mindfulness into my daily activities like driving and eating.

I learned so much from developing this workbook. There isn't a road map to happiness, and while it's always the ultimate goal, it's not always the ultimate destination. Increasing compassion for yourself, others, and life's events will inherently allow laughter and messiness to fill in those places once inhabited by unrealistic expectations.

My hope is that you have a mindful pregnancy, that you feel each kick and movement for its wonder and awe. This life inside you will never be there again. You have a limited opportunity to engage with all that's happening mentally and physically.

Congratulations! I am excited for you and the journey that has begun.

THEMES OF CULTIVATING YOUR HAPPINESS

While completing all the activities in this workbook will maximize the benefits connected to happiness and a more mindful pregnancy – this is your book! Use it how you want. Read it front to back, do something you're in the mood for in that moment, or focus on one of these individual themes at a time.

Creativity

Engaging in creative activities can decrease depressive feelings, increase positive emotions, reduce stress responses, and, in some cases, even improve immune system functioning. Throughout this book, I've included several creativity activities to help you slow down and focus on creating something, while also giving you an opportunity to show your uniqueness. Creating art allows us to live more fully and experience transformation.

Gratitude

Research continues to confirm that gratitude practices can outperform mood-enhancing medication, without the negative side effects. An intentional gratitude practice directly relates to increased happiness and will help deepen your social relationships, increase optimism, decrease materialism, and decrease stress. Utilize this book to cultivate your favorite gratitude activities and practices that you can take with you throughout your pregnancy and into motherhood.

Mindfulness

The mindfulness techniques introduced in this book will help you observe your thoughts, feelings, and sensations with an objective view. Mindfulness is shown to reduce stress, increase positive behavior, increase emotional regulation and increase better sleep habits. While meditation is a type of mindfulness practice (and several options are included within these pages), mindfulness focuses on being present and doesn't have to involve sitting quietly and counting your breath.

Positivity

A positive outlook enables you to cope better with stressful situations, which reduces the harmful health effects of stress on your body. The Mayo Clinic has proven that the ability to think more positively can have incredible benefits like increased lifespan, decreased risk of depression, a stronger immune system, and better psychological and physical well-being. You'll have opportunities to reframe thought patterns and create habits of positive thinking as you complete this workbook.

Social Connection

Utilize these activities to strengthen your current relationships, and hone the skills you need to create new ones. Well-being and overall happiness are closely tied with social connection and the relationships that we rely on regularly.

You are not
required to

SET
YOURSELF
ON FIRE

to keep other
people warm.

UNKNOWN

PREGNANCY CHALLENGE

In the box, tally each time you successfully accomplished the task.

Eat all of your meals without your cell phone									
Watch a movie from start to finish without your cell phone									
Enjoy your commute without checking your cell phone									
Listen to a music album from start to finish without distractions									
Rather than Googling, look something up in the newspaper or call a friend									

REFLECTIONS

FORGIVENESS

letting yourself off the hook.

We all make mistakes and are often the hardest on ourselves. Take the time to forgive yourself for five things you have been holding onto.

.01

.02

.03

.04

.05

what is your definition of beauty?

I FELT MY LUNGS
INFLATE WITH THE
ONRUSH OF SCENERY—
AIR, MOUNTAINS, TREES,
PEOPLE. I THOUGHT,

THIS

IS WHAT IT IS
TO BE HAPPY.

meditative word search

beauty
intention
love
family
heart
child
laughter
memories
lessons
experiences
connection
tradition
cuddles
baby
balance
breathe
hold
happiness
start
belly
self
kisses
gratitude
transformation
belief
hugs
calmness
peace
truth
awe
smile
mother
life

```
H Q P S N Q S E C A E P O Y S A U
G B R A E U T B X Y O I N A V Y C
A Z E O B P A W R N E H O L D E A
O R S L G O R J E O Y K I U I U L
E W U N L Z T H D I O O T N G V M
F S L T O Y R T B T W I C V A T N
A M X N S V M U T I H L E C W E E
K I S S E S Z R I D V N H E O S
J L I A L V L T R A B A N M F G S
G E L M Y E B I S R V S O Y A S D
R I S T K H E A R T M Y C E V A B
A E N D O L A E B O U E V L R N A
T H M M W O U G I Y R D H E R H I
I V H U G S T H E D B A T S I I J
T S O C L R Y N A Y C H E S E L E
U G Y O X U L J L L G Z A O A O S
D F A F L E S G D U C I U N L I E
E T E S G K A V A D I T O S C J I
N L M A U D T L B Y L I F E L H R
J B E L I E F E Y Z V Y R Y G R O
A U Q P F E L I W T E N T I O N M
B R L H U Y X C D D L I H C E B E
K S B A L F K E Q G T Y K A D R M
C E X P E R I E N C E S F Q Y P K
E V D P O T U B R E H L J A N E L
H O N I T W I I T J Y E I E O N E
T L V N O I T A M R O F S N A R T
A U O E I K S L X N H I T P U S O
E T T S C J J W E C U D D L E S P
R D O S T N D A M O T H E R B M I
B A L A N C E F S Y R O M C L O B
E U P E U M Y L I M A F S N O D A
```

AWE(SOME) WALK

Awe is defined as a brain stimulation when we experience something overwhelmingly beautiful.

challenge Take time to explore new places outside (downtown, parks, trails, etc.) in search of things, creatures, and activities that bring you awe.

rules Turn off your cell phone, put on your childhood glasses and see the world with a fresh perspective. Go somewhere new each time! Write about each exploration:

appreciating appreciation

Write down every time you are thanked until the page is full.

J.K.

We do not need magic to
transform our world.

WE CARRY ALL THE POWER WE NEED INSIDE OURSELVES ALREADY:

we have the power
to imagine better

ROWLING

GIFTING GRATITUDE

No one has ever said, "I am thanked too much."
Spreading gratitude is easy, contagious and fun.

challenge Create a goal for yourself each day to see how many people you can thank. Think of those individuals who rarely get any appreciation: the mailman, interns, parents, etc.

rules You cannot just say "thank you." You must develop a thoughtful and personalized message (or gift if inclined) for each person you will gift with gratitude. Write about your five experiences.

.01

.02

.03

.04

.05

dear diary:
Write a diary entry as though you found out you were pregnant today.

CANDLE MEDITATION

Create a quiet and dimly lit environment to try candle meditation. The goal is to practice focusing. Stare at the flame. Notice the movement. Pay attention to the color. Envision yourself as the flame. Gaze into the dancing light. What sounds does the flame create? Enjoy the peace and calmness.

BENEFITS

Candle meditation is a simple exercise to begin a meditation practice. It can improve mental stability, lower stress and strengthen your ability to focus for longer periods of time. Start with a goal of three minutes and develop the capacity to focus longer and longer at each attempt.

THE GOAL OF MEDITATION ISN'T TO CONTROL YOUR THOUGHTS, IT'S TO STOP THEM FROM CONTROLLING YOU.

The Age of Enlightenment

WHEN YOU'RE
A CHILD,
ANYTHING *&*
EVERYTHING
IS POSSIBLE.
THE CHALLENGE,
SO OFTEN,
IS HANGING
ON TO THAT
AS WE GROW UP.

MINDFULNESS

Take a solo adventure and write about it.

solo inspiration

TRY A NEW RESTAURANT

GO TO THE PARK

WALK A NEW ROUTE

CHECK OUT A MOVIE

ENJOY A CONCERT

VISIT A MUSEUM

TOUR THE ZOO

TAKE A ROAD TRIP

VOLUNTEER

GO TO THE FARMERS MARKET

TRY AN ART CLASS

TEST OUT IMPROV

CHEER ON A SPORTS TEAM

READ A BOOK OUTSIDE

PICNIC FOR ONE

RIDE A BIKE

BOOK A SPA DAY

GO SWIMMING

PEOPLE WATCH

PAINT A PICTURE

COOK A NEW RECIPE

POSITIVE SELF-TALK

be kind to yourself

Restate each of these negative self-talk expressions into positive terms. Next, say them to yourself in the mirror.

.01   *I look fat.*

.02   *I am not prepared to be a mom.*

.03   *I will not be as good as the other moms.*

.04   *I don't have time for self-care.*

.05   *I'm not strong enough.*

MEDITATION BREATHING EXERCISES

Meditation is often misunderstood. The intention does not have to be to eliminate all thoughts. The goal is to work (regularly) on controlling your thoughts. The easiest way to begin a meditation practice is to focus on your breathing.

Close your eyes and breathe in and out. Take really slow, deep breaths. How does it make you feel? How deeply can you breathe? Notice your stomach and chest as you inhale and exhale. How does the baby react to your calming breaths?

Whenever a thought, worry, or idea pops into your focus, just imagine writing it down on a piece of paper and flying it away like a paper airplane. You may also choose to imagine the thought being erased on a chalkboard. Either way, it is fine to acknowledge the thought and then simply send it away. Focus your attention back to your breath.

Although it sounds simple, it can be very difficult. We live in a world of constant action and distraction. Don't give up! Every single time you sit down and focus on your breath, you are training your brain (like any other muscle). You can't expect to go to the gym and use 50-lb dumbbells for biceps curls on your first day.

Taking time to meditate will help you and baby. Slow breathing reduces stress and helps build internal resilience. Plus, you might want to enjoy every quiet second you can before your child arrives.

ABSORB IT

Taking compliments can be difficult.

challenge Write down the next five compliments you
receive.

rules Truly take time to list, absorb and embrace each kind
word.

MINDFULNESS CHALLENGE

In the box, tally each time you successfully accomplished the task.

Waking up: Before getting out of bed, think of 3 things you are excited about.												
Tea time: While drinking coffee or tea, eliminate all distractions and focus on the nutrients you are receiving.												
Connect with nature: Keep a flower or plant close by, each day try to notice its new growth and beauty.												
Stretch: Make it a routine to stretch after each trip to the restroom (this could be frequently).												
Walking: Notice your pace and stride. Pay attention to the ground and your movements.												

REFLECTIONS

Hard work plus bravery equals

SUCCESS

Imagination plus bravery equals

CREATIVITY

Love plus bravery equals

HAPPINESS

HOBSON

MINDFULNESS

Think about how you have changed positively since becoming pregnant.

reflect on this growth.

ASSERTIVENESS

Assertiveness is the ability to express your feelings and ask for what you want. Let's practice developing effective assertive communication tools. Use the space to write "I" statements. Don't be afriad to share your feelings and be honest.

example   I don't like unsolicited parenting
advice. I want to try things my way.

I STATEMENTS

GRATITUDE CHALLENGE

You don't have to spend a lot of money to value something. Think about the different things you hold dear to your heart. List those in the categories below.

Items less than $250	
Items less than $100	
Items less than $50	
Items less than $25	
Items less than $10	

REFLECTIONS

THE SECRET
TO HAVING IT ALL
IS BELIEVING YOU
ALREADY DO.

UNKNOWN

FOUR STEPS TO SELF-FORGIVENESS

1. WHAT | I want to forgive myself for...

2. ACKNOWLEGDE | I now choose to release my feelings of ...

3. BENEFIT | I acknowledge that forgiving myself will help me feel:

4. COMMITMENT | I commit to forgive myself and acccept peace...

MINDFULNESS

playful playlist

Curate a positive playlist for your ideal birth:

inspiration

DAUGHTERS
John Mayer

HAVEN'T MET YOU YET
Michael Buble

HEY HO
Lumineers

SUNRISE
Norah Jones

ALL OF ME
John Legend

NAKED AS WE CAME
Iron and Wine

DON'T LEAVE ME
Regina Spektor

HALLELUJAH
Jeff Buckley

HOLD YOU IN MY ARMS
Ray LaMontagne

GLORIOUS
Macklemore

STOLEN DANCE
Milky Chance

DELICATE
Damien Rice

SIMPLIFY

We often allow material possessions to control us. The simple act of letting go can cause more room internally for mindfulness. See what things you can donate to others in need: clothing, household items, and anything tangible that doesn't bring you joy or purpose.

GIVE TIME

Do you ever think about volunteering but haven't made time to do so? You have unique skills and abilities that could help change others' lives, so share them! Research shows that helping others generates a significant boost in personal satisfaction and happiness. Sit down and do some research to find people and projects in your community to which you can lend your time.

COLOR MEDITATION

Take a routine part of your day (such as driving to work) and focus your attention on a specific color. Each day, pick a new color and try to find that color throughout your routine. You'll find yourself discovering new things you've overlooked. Taking time to focus trains your brain to slow down. In time, you'll develop new processes for taking in information that is more complete and robust. Meditation in any form helps build mental resilience.

CULTIVATE THE HABIT OF ZEST.
PURPOSEFULLY SEEK OUT THE BEAUTY IN
THE SEEMINGLY TRIVIAL. ESPECIALLY IN
THE TRIVIAL. THE COLORS AND SHAPES
OF THE FOODS YOU EAT. THE SHADOWS
A VASE MAKES ON YOUR TABLE. THE
INTERESTING FACES OF THE PEOPLE ON
THE BUS WITH YOU.

— Karen Solmansohn

MINDFULNESS

You have something to say. Imagine you are writing a book.
What story do you need to share with the world?

book description

author bio

KINDNESS IN WORDS
CREATES CONFIDENCE.
KINDNESS IN
THINKING CREATES
PROFOUNDNESS.
KINDNESS IN GIVING
CREATES LOVE.

UNKNOWN

PHOTO SEARCH

challenge You are tasked with digging into your personal photos to uncover joy and wonder.

rules Using your phone or photo album, seek out multiple photos that include the following themes and note why you selected the specific photo.

compassion

awe

positivity

gratitude

love

SMILE MEDITATION

When in public, make it a game to see how many people you can get to smile back at you. Smile at each stranger who passes you by, focusing on sharing your positive energy. A smile can truly change someone's day. Just think about how great your day will be with all the smiles coming back at you.

CARRY OUT A RANDOM ACT OF KINDNESS, WITH NO EXPECTATION OF REWARD, SAFE IN THE KNOWLEDGE THAT ONE DAY SOMEONE MIGHT DO THE SAME FOR YOU.

Princess Diana

what do you feel strongly about right now?

MEANINGFUL PLACE MEDITATION

When was the last time you went back to your elementary school, your first job, or the place you met your significant other? Take time and plan a trip to revisit a meaningful place in your life. If possible, share the experience with someone you love. Share why and how this place is significant and embedded in your heart.

Who were you when you were last there? What specfic memories does the place evoke? How did this experience strengthen you? How has the place changed?

BENEFITS

Revisiting past experiences can both deepen a memory of an event or place in time, and can also help your brain recall additional memories and experiences. Our brains are so often caught in the recall and replaying of negative experiences that we forget about the positive and life-changing ones.

STORYTELLING

Stories can be the best medium for authenic human connection. Stories engage us with emotions, meaning and purpose. Storytelling is commonly used to heal from life's events. Science proves that stories engage our imagination and deepen empathy for others.

challenge Take time to sit down and hear another woman's story. There is something to learn from everyone.

rules Listen more than you speak. Validate their experience by showing compassion. Reflect on five things you learned from the conversation.

.01

.02

.03

.04

.05

THE MIND
IS JUST LIKE
A MUSCLE.

THE MORE YOU
EXERCISE IT,

THE STRONGER
IT GETS AND
THE MORE
IT CAN

E X P A N D

SOCIAL CONNECTIONS

If your best friend is pregnant and experiencing struggles with accepting her new pregnancy physique and limitations, what would you say to her?

Now, are you telling your friend anything different than what you are telling yourself?

SOCIAL CONNECTION

inquisitive interview
Ask someone to share their knowledge with you:

question prompts:

WHAT MAKES YOU HAPPY?

WHEN WAS YOUR LAST CRY?

NEWEST PASSION?

DO YOU BELIEVE IN SOULMATES?

HOW DO YOU DEFINE SUCCESS?

BEST GIFT YOU'VE RECIEVED?

WHO IS YOUR ROLE MODEL?

WHAT DOES YOUR FUTURE HOLD?

HOW HAS SOMEONE IMPACTED YOU?

CAN PEOPLE CHANGE?

WHAT MAKES A FRIEND?

DEFINITION OF MOTHERHOOD?

WHAT IS YOUR FAVORITE BOOK?

ARE YOU SPIRITUAL?

WHAT WAS YOUR CHILDHOOD LIKE?

HOW DO YOU LEARN?

PERSONAL RITUAL?

DO YOU HAVE A GRATITUDE PRACTICE?

DEFINING MOMENT?

SOUNDS

Have you ever spent time listening to the noises around you? One peaceful way to meditate is to focus on the sounds around your environment.

challenge Sit still and listen to the sounds around you. Pick five different opportunities to tune in.

rules Listen without distractions. Detail your experience below.

.01

.02

.03

.04

.05

ANNIE

How we spend our days is, of course, how we spend our lives.

DILLARD

MINDFULNESS

what creation are you most proud of?

Style is not labels or trends. Having impeccable style is feeling
confident in your clothing. How has your clothing and accessories
changed since becoming pregnant?

pre-bump style	pregnancy style

CONTAGIOUS

Positivity is contagious, see if you can spread it like a wild fire.

challenge Build five people's self-esteem and confidence today. Go on social media and seek out connections who may need some extra love. Who else is pregnant? Who needs a smile?

rules Use various social media tools to positively engage. Write a personalized compliment where it can publically be viewed for all to see in the digital world. Give unsolicited kudos. (You don't have to stop at five people...).

.01

.02

.03

.04

.05

pregnancy is powerful. pregnancy is precious. pregnancy is positive. pregnancy is productive. pregnancy is patient. pregnancy is peaceful. pregnancy is perfect. pregnancy is personable. pregnancy is playful. pregnancy is pleasant. pregnancy is plenty. pregnancy is pretty. pregnancy is priceless. pregnancy is proficient. pregnancy is prominent. pregnancy is proud. pregnancy is perfect. pregnancy is personable. pregnancy is prosperous. pregnancy is pure. pregnancy is powerful. pregnancy is precious. pregnancy is positive. pregnancy is productive. pregnancy is patient. pregnancy is peaceful. pregnancy is perfect. pregnancy is personable. pregnancy is playful. pregnancy is pleasant. pregnancy is plenty. pregnancy is pretty. pregnancy is priceless. pregnancy is proficient. pregnancy is prominent. pregnancy is proud. pregnancy is perfect. pregnancy is personable. pregnancy is prosperous. pregnancy is pure. pregnancy is powerful. pregnancy is pure. pregnancy is powerful. pregnancy is precious. pregnancy is positive. pregnancy is productive. pregnancy is patient. pregnancy is peaceful. pregnancy is perfect. pregnancy is personable. pregnancy is playful. pregnancy is pleasant. pregnancy is plenty. pregnancy is pretty. pregnancy is priceless. pregnancy is proficient. pregnancy is prominent. pregnancy is proud. pregnancy is perfect. pregnancy is personable. pregnancy is prosperous. pregnancy is pure. pregnancy is powerful. pregnancy is pure. pregnancy is powerful. pregnancy is precious. pregnancy is positive. pregnancy is productive. pregnancy is patient. pregnancy is peaceful. pregnancy is perfect. pregnancy is personable. pregnancy is playful. pregnancy is pleasant. pregnancy is plenty. pregnancy is pretty. pregnancy is priceless. pregnancy is proficient. pregnancy is prominent. pregnancy is proud. pregnancy is perfect. pregnancy is personable. pregnancy is prosperous. pregnancy is pure. pregnancy is powerful. pregnancy is pure. pregnancy is powerful. pregnancy is precious. pregnancy is positive. pregnancy is productive. pregnancy is patient. pregnancy is peaceful. pregnancy is ... pregnancy is personable. pregnancy is playful. pregnancy is pleasant. pregnancy is plenty. pregnancy is pretty. pregnancy is priceless. pregnancy is proficient. pregnancy is

define motherhood in only positive
words. don't stop until the page is full.

Life shrinks
or expands in
proportion to
one's courage.

CREATIVITY

Get out your glue sticks. It's time to create a vision board for your remaining pregnancy. Curate things that represent your ideal mood and mindset in the box below.

POSITIVITY

When things don't add up, start subtracting. What do you need to remove
from your daily clutter (people, places, or things) for less stress?

remove	solution

REROUTING

Do you take the same route to the grocery store each trip? Do you run the same errands and go to the same places routinely?

When you do something on repeat, your brain goes into auto-pilot. You don't see new things and develop new experiences unless you get out of your comfort zone.

For the next week, try to drive a new route to the usual places you go. Take the scenic route. While grocery shopping, start on the opposite side you typically begin with. Walk instead of driving.

What do you notice? Are you more present? Has it caused you to think differently? Does it feel uncomfortable or strange?

LEARNING CHALLENGE

Challenge yourself to complete the following mediums before baby is born. Check each time you complete something.

Books										
Podcasts										
Poems										
Music Albums										
Documentaries										

FAVORITES

DINNER DATE

imagine your ideal meal.

Tapping into our desired actions, thoughts, and feelings allows us to create a meaningful relationship with food and how we eat.

Write about your ideal dinner date.

FOOD TO BE SERVED

MUSIC TO BE PLAYING

GUESTS AROUND THE TABLE

LOCATION OF MEAL

EMOTIONS EVOKED

WALKING MEDITATION

Who knew you could walk while meditating? That changes the stereotype that you have to sit and be quiet and remove all thoughts. Walking meditation has been shown to assist with anxious thinking and promotes cognitive thinking to enhance productivity.

Make the sidewalk your runway. Pay attention to your stride, your pace, how you feet feel to hit the ground, how you breathe, and how each muscle contracts. Connect your mind and body through intentional walking.

How would you describe the change in your walk when being focused and intentional.

WE EITHER LIVE WITH INTENTION OR EXIST BY DEFAULT.

Kristin Armstrong

CREATIVITY

Give yourself a pat on the back (or belly). You deserve it. In the
space below, draw a trophy for all the kudos you have earned.

SOCIAL BUCKET LIST

Consider this your "I've been meaning to do" list.

challenge Live larger and strive to live life with no regrets. Write down five social things you want to do before baby comes.

example Have you always wanted to take up pasta making or join a knitting club? Or maybe you have been thinking about reaching out to an old friend whom you have lost touch with over the years.

EMOTIONAL CHALLENGE

Emotional awareness is an often neglected skill. Some studies show that only 1 in 3 of us has the ability to correctly assess our feelings. Track your emotions for one week.

Excited											
Happy											
Anxious											
Scared											
Sad											

REFLECTIONS

SOCIAL CONNECTION

Reflection brings perspective. Using your phone or photo album, find
the following photos. Do you notice a theme within your photos?

scavenger hunt:

AN INCREDIBLE
OUTFIT

A MOMENT YOU
WERE CONFIDENT

A FRIEND WHO IS
HAPPY

DELICIOUS FOOD

A SWEET ANIMAL

BEAUTIFUL
SCENERY

A GROUP OF
FRIENDS

A COUPLE IN LOVE

SOMEONE
ENJOYING
SOLITUDE

A MEMORY YOU'VE
FORGOTTEN

A CELEBRATORY
GATHERING

POOR
PHOTOGRAPHY
SKILLS

SOMETHING
UNIQUE

A COMMON PLACE

GENUINE SMILES

A DEFINITION OF
LOVE

A CASUAL
GATHERING

A JOYOUS
MILESTONE

what physical items do you possess that you truly appreciate?

GROWTH
&COMFORT
never coexist.

RADIO SHOW

you are hosting a radio show

You've landed a lucrative contract to host your own radio show. Think about how you'd develop the show to showcase what you're passionate about.

RADIO SHOW TAGLINE

POTENTIAL CO-HOSTS

GUESTS TO INTERVIEW

POTENTIAL SPONSORS/ COMMERCIALS

MUSIC TO BE PLAYED

you have enough. you are enough. you do enough.
you have enough. you are enough. you do enough.
you have enough. you are enough. you do enough.
you have enough. you are enough. you do enough.
you have enough. you are enough. you do enough.
you have enough. you are enough. you do enough.
you have enough. you are enough. you do enough.
you have enough. you are enough. you do enough.
you have enough. you are enough. you do enough.
you have enough. you are enough. you do enough.
you have enough. you are enough. you do enough.
you have enough. you are enough. you do enough.
you have enough. you are enough. you do enough.
you have enough. you are enough. you do enough.
you have enough. you are enough. you do enough.
you have enough. you are enough. you do enough.
you have enough. you are enough. you do enough.
you have enough. you are enough. you do enough.
you have enough. you are enough. you do enough.
you have enough. you are enough. you do enough.
you have enough. you are enough. you do enough.
you have enough. you are enough. you do enough.
you have enough. you are enough. you do enough.
you have enough. you are enough. you do enough.
you have enough. you are enough. you do enough.
you have enough. you are enough. you do enough.
you have enough. you are enough. you do enough.
you have enough. you are enough. you do enough.

ORDINARY OBJECTS

Find five ordinary objects and reflect on ways in which they are beautiful.

.01	
.02	
.03	
.04	
.05	

WHAT IS BEAUTIFUL YET ORDINARY ABOUT PREGNANCY?

spontaneous spirit

What spontaneous adventure can you attempt right now and reflect on?

spontaneous ideas:

SHOW UP AT A
FRIEND'S DOORSTEP

DELIVER SURPRISE
BAKED GOODS

BOOK A LAST-MINUTE
HOTEL

GET A MANICURE

INVITE FRIENDS OVER

TRY A NEW
RESTAURANT

GO BOWLING

HIKE A NEW TRAIL

PICK OUT A NEW
GENRE BOOK

CALL A FRIEND AND
SING TO THEM

PICK A NEW RECIPE
AND MAKE IT

BUY A NEW OUTFIT

DO YOUR HAIR AND
MAKEUP LIKE PROM

DRIVE WITHOUT A
DESTINATION

VISIT A PARK

GO SWIMMING

DROP IN ON A
COLLEGE CLASS

TRY NEW DANCE
MOVES

do you replay past conversations in your head? use the space below to change past conversations to clear your head.

MYTH BUSTING

Write down the truth against the following pregnancy myths.

pregnancy is forever	
birth is unsafe	
you'll be emotional	
you'll never be the same	
advice is needed	

WHAT MYTHS HAVE YOU FEARED?

STRENGTHS
what are your strengths?

challenge Ask five people in your life to describe a unique strength and how you showcase that strength throughout your life and your pregnancy.

rules Write down the responses and digest the wonderful affirmations from those in your life.

IF YOU'RE NOT HAPPY
TODAY, THEN YOU WON'T
BE HAPPY TOMORROW
UNLESS YOU TAKE THINGS
INTO YOUR OWN HANDS
AND TAKE ACTION.

be a storyteller. finish the rest of the narrative:
she sat, one hand on her belly to feel the life inside her...

GREENERY MEDITATION

Find a local garden or floral shop to spend some time strolling around.
Be mindful of the plants and the flowers.

QUESTIONS TO CONSIDER

What smells like happiness to you? Pregnancy could even alter your
preferences to smells. Spot a flower that resembles your pregnancy. Is there
a plant that inspires you? Look for how many different shades of green you
can identify. What has this location done to your breathing? How slow can you
walk around?

BENEFITS

By consciously savoring beautiful things around us, we are then able
to identify and acknowledge beautiful things in the future. We are
reprogramming our brains to look for positive things instead of the common
negative mentality. Trying something new gets us out of our typical routine.
This helps for the new-mom brain too!

**I DECIDED THAT IF I COULD PAINT THAT
FLOWER IN SUCH A HUGE SCALE, YOU COULD
NOT IGNORE ITS BEAUTY.**

Georgia O'Keefe

VACATION

plan your ideal vacation!

If money and time didn't matter, let's plan your ideal vacation. Think through how you prefer to refuel by choosing your vacation details:

LOCATION

WEATHER

TRAVEL PARTNER

ACTIVITIES

VACATION EMOTIONS

DREAM TEAM

challenge Imagine that you are able to give the most important presentation of your life. Think about who are five people who you could count on to be your dream team.

bonus Tell each person why you need them in your life and how they bring out the best in you.

POSITIVE WORDS

Write down 12 positive words about yourself and your pregnancy.

.01	
.02	
.03	
.04	
.05	
.06	
.07	
.08	
.09	
.10	
.11	
.12	

MALALA

ONE CHILD
ONE TEACHER
ONE BOOK
ONE PEN

can change the world

YOUSAFZAI

you're writing an article for a pregnancy magazine on how to enjoy your pregnancy, give your expert advice below.

EQUATIONS

For those who love math, one plus one equals two. However, some of us like to be more creative with our math skills. Let's create some more imaginative equations.

examples: yoga + essential oils = calmness   cake + broccoli = pregnant breakfast

_____ + _____ = _____

_____ + _____ = _____

_____ + _____ = _____

_____ + _____ = _____

_____ + _____ = _____

REFLECTIONS

SILENCE MEDITATION

"Everything that's created comes out of silence. Thoughts emerge from the nothingness of silence. Words come out of that void. Your very essence emerged from emptiness. All creativity requires some stillness."
-Wayne Dyer

When was the last time you sat in silence?

Silence can be an incredible teacher. Silence teaches us to tune into our bodies and thoughts.

Try it. Sit quietly in a space with little noises or distractions. Is the silence enjoyable or uncomfortable? How long can you sit in the silence? What did you learn?

WORDS CAN BE TWISTED INTO ANY SHAPE. PROMISES CAN BE MADE TO LULL THE HEART AND SEDUCE THE SOUL. IN THE FINAL ANALYSIS, WORDS MEAN NOTHING. THEY ARE LABELS WE GIVE THINGS IN AN EFFORT TO WRAP OUR PUNY LITTLE BRAINS AROUND THEIR UNDERLYING NATURES, WHEN NINETY-NINE PERCENT OF THE TIME THE TOTALITY OF THE REALITY IS AN ENTIRELY DIFFERENT BEAST. THE WISEST MAN IS THE SILENT ONE. EXAMINE HIS ACTIONS. JUDGE HIM BY THEM.

Karen Marie Moning

DEFINING

more than one meaning

Define each word with two separate definitions. Ask your social network if you need various opinions.

PREGNANT

FEMININE

COMMUNITY

HAPPINESS

FUTURE

CREATIVITY

Color in each of the six components of health by your
perceived fullness in each category.

EMOTIONAL

ENVIRONMENTAL

SPRITUAL

MENTAL

SOCIAL

PHYSICAL

MARIANNE

OUR DEEPEST FEAR

IS NOT THAT WE ARE

INADEQUATE,

IT IS THAT WE ARE

POWERFUL

BEYOND

MEASURE

WILLIAMSON

reflect on a time when you surprised yourself?

SOCIAL CONNECTION

happiness challenge
Spend the day trying to put others first. reflect on how you felt.

SENSES

"Of the five senses, smell is the one with the best memory."
- Rebecca McClanahan

For some women, smell is heightened during pregnancy. Try to tune into your sense smell to deepen your memory of your time being pregnant.

THINK ABOUT THE FOLLOWING QUESTIONS:

What scents linger?
What smells stop you in your tracks?
What smell to you want to remember and associate with your pregnancy?

To help you remember to acknowledge the scents around you, set a random alarm each day to allow you to be present and smell your environment.

Circle the power words that define you.

free. focused. remarkable. confident.
wanted. obsessive. worker. doer. sizeable.
new. surging. mom. wonderful. professional.
guaranteed. interesting. special. challenging.
daughter. unique. tested. talented. improved.
simplistic. limited. simplistic. powerful.
big. popular. friend. exclusive. valuable.
endorsed. fundamental. skilled. better.
useful. authentic. female. practical. expert.
colorful. ultimate. willpowered. attractive.
competitive. innovative. fierce. soaring.
beautiful. astonishing. imaginative. exciting.
amazing. sensational. excellent. advocate. edgy.
feminine. pioneering. unconditional.
magical. weird. delighted. timely. famous.
strong. energetic. unusual. instructive. rare.
liberal. superior. fascinating. helpful. successful.
opportunistic. monumental. quick. easy.
simple. strange. direct. pregnant.

comfort zones confine us. what has pregnancy taught you about stretching beyond your norm?

YOU REALLY HAVE TO LOVE YOURSELF TO GET ANYTHING DONE IN THIS WORLD.

MINDFULNESS

Our daily routines can take over and diminish our intended priorities.
Detail how much time you spend doing specific activities and then
consider how you'd like to reallocate your time.

CURRENT ROUTINE

Forgiveness is
a skill. Practice
forgiveness first
with youself. By
learning to let
go of the little
things, you'll
be able deepen
relationships.

DESIRED ROUTINE

NOTHING EVER GOES
AWAY UNTIL IT HAS
TAUGHT US WHAT WE
NEED TO KNOW.

**PEMA
CHODRON**

OVERDUE CALLS

When was the last time you sat down and thought about calling an old friend? Maybe someone from school or an old neighbor? Do you have loved ones that would love to hear your voice and appreciate an update on your pregnancy?

challenge:

Scroll through your phone and select four people to call. Note how you both felt about the call.

.01

.02

.03

.04

"We become what we think about." -Earl Nightingale

You must first envision something beautiful before it can be created.
Below, design your desired pregnancy.
Try using markers, magazines, paint, makeup, or anything you choose.

CREATIVITY

Can you go an entire weekend without spending money? See if you
can do it and reflect on your experience below.

free activity ideas

GO TO THE LIBRARY

WALK THE MALL

CREATE A PICNIC
FROM PANTRY ITEMS

OFFER TO WALK A
DOG

HOST A YARD SALE

PICK WEEDS FOR A
NEIGHBOR

VISIT THE ANIMAL
SHELTER

PEOPLE WATCH AT
THE PARK

DO A PHOTOSHOOT

HOST A TRASH
PICKUP

VOLUNTEER AT A
SENIOR HOME

ORGANIZE PHOTO
ALBUMS

WASH YOUR CAR AT
HOME

HOST A SKYPE
PARTY

NETFLIX MARATHON

SPRING CLEAN
YOUR CLOTHES

TOUR A NEW
NEIGHBORHOOD

BABYSIT FOR A
FRIEND

does being pregnant change how you view your mother?

The more we see, the more we are capable of seeing.

MEDIA CHALLENGE

Self-care can include electronic media and hand-held devices. Mark each time you use electronic devices for self-care.

Podcasts												
Favorite tv show												
Movie throwback												
Audio book												
Positive social media use												

HOW CAN YOU POSITIVELY USE MEDIA?

SELF-LOVE

treat yourself to self-love

What five activities do you need to allow yourself more
time to do? What replenishes your pregnant energy?

.01

.02

.03

.04

.05

MINDFULNESS

Body language communicates more than spoken language. Since your child cannot verbally communicate for some time, try to hone in on your nonverbal skills.

challenge:

Make note of what people are expressing when they aren't speaking. Secondly, how much can you express throughout your day without speaking? Try it and reflect.

"IT ISN'T WHAT WE SAY OR THINK THAT DEFINES US, BUT WHAT WE DO."

Jane Austen

LISTENING POWER

When was the last time you felt heard? So often, we listen to respond and fix, rather than having the true intention of listening to understand. The best way to be heard is to listen. Listen before responding.

CHALLENGE

Engage in a conversation with a loved one with the intent to listen. Sit next to each other without furniture between you and eliminate any technology devices. Start first by sharing something vulnerable using "I" statements. For example, "I feel sad and uncomfortable because I'm overworked at my job," instead of saying "word is hard." By using "I" statements, you have full ownership of your statement. Only share when your stomach has butterflies and you feel compelled to speak, not to fill the voids.

When you listen, do not respond with words at all, no advice, no reciprocal stories or affirmations. Respond only with your presence and energy of acceptance. The silence is powerful and allows each participant the ability to think in a meaningful way.

what element of pregnancy do you need to better embrace?

ELLA

THE ONLY THING
better THAN singing,
IS MORE *singing.*

FITZGERALD

WOULD YOU RATHER?

Although there are no wrong answers, circle below which self-care activity is more your style.

COFFEE *or* TEA

YOGA *or* RUNNING

NEWS *or* COMICS

NON-FICTION *or* FICTION

BOOK *or* MAGAZINE

SHOWER *or* BATH

PEDICURE *or* MANICURE

STAND *or* SIT

LISTEN *or* TALK

GIVE *or* RECEIVE

LAUGH *or* CRY

GRATITUDE

The happiest people are profoundly grateful. Acknowledging your gratitude to others deepens relationships. When was the last time you received a handwritten thank you note? The art of thank you notes has disappeared in the digital age.

challenge:
Take time (with your feet propped up) to write as many thank you notes as you can in one hour. Below, make a list of people you need to thank.

"WHEN WE WITNESS GREAT ACTS OF KINDNESS OR COURAGE, IT INSPIRES US AND ELEVATES US TO ALSO WANT TO BE KINDER AND BRAVER OURSELVES."

Lea Waters

how do you know what love is? when have you felt loved?

YOU MUST
DO THE THING
YOU THINK
YOU CANNOT DO

SOCIAL CONNECTION

Celebrating holidays and birthdays is a great way to spend time with those you love. for some, gift giving is a love language. Begin to think about the gifts and recipients you have on your list for the rest of the year:

inspiration

FRAMED PHOTO

BAKED GOODS

HANDMADE ART

CURATED PLAYLIST

FLOWERS

BOARD GAME

FAMILY CALENDAR

SPECIAL TRIP

JOURNAL

INSTRUCTIONAL CLASS

QUALITY TIME

CHORE CERTIFICATE

POEM

BASKET OF FAVORITE THINGS

JEWELRY

SPA TREATMENT

SCAVENGER HUNT

CHOCOLATE

SINGING TELEGRAM

CHILDHOOD TOY

CUSTOM WORDSEARCH

BOOK BY FAVORITE AUTHOR

HOUSEKEEPING

CONCERT TICKETS

YIELDING TO KINDNESS

We all need kindness to survive, it's like breathing. Being kind to yourself allows you to practice and experience giving and receiving of such joy.

Giving kindness to others can be fun and exciting. However, when are we intentional about giving kindness to ourselves? When do we reflect on moments when we were kind? When do we thank ourselves when we are gentle and patient with ourselves?

CHALLENGE

Create a prompt that reminds you to grant yourself thanks or to acknowledge your inner kindness. For example, every single time that you see a yield sign, think about being kinder to yourself. What can you forgive yourself for? Do you need to congratulate yourself? Use the large yellow sign as a positive mechanism to routinely yield kindness to yourself. The yield sign is optional, pick something that is routine yet stands out such as a "closed for business" sign or your gas tank on empty.

CREATIVITY

Have you ever noticed that cartoon characters always wear the same outfit?
Pregnancy can also give us an opportunity to connect to several staple wardrobe
options. In the space below, draw your pregnancy cartoon outfit.

TRANSFORMATION

challenge Think about the pivotal societal events or personal events that have defined your life. Write about how those events have transformed you into the person you are today.

we have gone back in time five years...
you just found out that you are pregnant, how do you feel?

I refuse to be
called a victim.

I am not defined by
what happened in my life.

I am a survivor, defined
by how I live my life.

MUSICAL MEMORIES

challenge — Scan the radio (or favorite streaming service) and stop on a random song. Write down the very first vivid and specific memory that comes to mind.

example — The song may remind you of your best friend's last birthday party. At the birthday party you....

POWER OF LANGUAGE

In school, our English teachers tried to create a love of poetry. As adults however, that love can fade. Language becomes practical rather than fanciful, and we may start to think of words not as amusing sounds we make but rather as tools we can put to use. While it's true this practical side of language has great power, it also has its limits. Reading and writing poetry allow us to explore what lies beyond these limits, to remind ourselves that language is not just something we learn; it's something we actively take part in making.

Spend 20 minutues finding a poem that speaks to you in this stage of pregnancy. You can go to the library, ask a friend, or use the internet to spark some poetic pregnancy justice.

Then, share your favorite poem with someone else. Ask them what they took from the poem and share why you selected it.

what does the word 'birth' mean to you?

CREATIVITY

Find your favorite piece of art (if you don't have one yet, discover it now), print it off, cut it out, and tape it below. Write why it's your favorite.

MAKING VOWS

Vow to make prenatal self a priority. Make your vows meaningful, personal and timeless. Identify what personal vows you can commit to yourself.

I vow to always...	
I vow to have...	
I vow to share...	
I vow to not...	
I vow to help...	

REFLECTIONS

RACHEL

*ONE WAY TO OPEN YOUR
EYES IS TO ASK YOURSELF,*

WHAT IF *I HAD NEVER*
SEEN THIS BEFORE?

WHAT IF *I KNEW I WOULD*
NEVER SEE IT AGAIN?

CARSON

stream—of—consciousness writing:
set a timer and write without stopping for ten minutes.

5 SENSES CHALLENGE

Attempt to indulge all five senses for self-care.
Track yourself for reminders and motivation.

Sight (art musuem, beautiful walk, etc.)								
Hear (music, nature, quiet, etc.)								
Touch (blankets, animals, crafts, etc.)								
Smell (candles, food, flowers, etc.)								
Taste (food, spices, virgin cocktails, etc.)								

WHICH SENSE IS HEIGHTENED WHILE PREGNANT?

MINDFULNESS

Create a recipe for pregnancy since you are now an expert.

Items Needed for Mama and Baby Bump:
Example: Stretchy pants, comofortable pillows, etc.

Ingredients
Example:
Supportive friends

Directions:
Example: Begin by mixing together your excitement with your family.

SURROUNDED

be selective with who you surround yourself with

We become who we surround ourselves with. Who are
the five friends that you spend your time with? What do
they do to enhance your life? How have they positively
impacted you?

.01

.02

.03

.04

.05

what do you believe makes a strong female?
who in your life would you define as a strong female?

I believe that life should be lived so vividly and so intensely that thoughts of another life, or of a longer life, are not necessary.

POSITIVITY

If you could schedule the optimal pregnant day,
what would you do? Make your optimal day happen!

schedule

6AM

7AM

8AM

9AM

10AM

11AM

12PM

1PM

2PM

3PM

4PM

5PM

6PM

7PM

8PM

9PM

10PM

11PM

EMOTIONS

emotional recognition

In the space below, write what specific event or people can help you to feel the following emotions.

Happy

.01

Scared

.02

Proud

.03

Sad

.04

Anxious

.05

MINDFULNESS

Write the lyrics to the song that best resembles your pregnancy today:

inspiration

THE LUCKIEST
Ben Folds

EYE OF THE TIGER
Survivor

BEAUTIFUL BOY
John Lennon

COUNTDOWN
Beyonce

DOG DAYS ARE OVER
Florence and the Machine

**GONNA MAKE
YOU SWEAT**
C + C Music Factory

HAPPY
Pharrell

I'M COMING OUT
Diana Ross

ALL OF ME
John Legend

CLOSING TIME
Semisonic

STRONG ENOUGH
Cher

BRAVE
Sara Bareilles

SPECTRUMS

self—awareness allows understanding

Circle where you belong on the following specturms.
Number 1 is considered very low and number 10 is
considered very high, most like you.

PATIENT   01 02 03 04 05 06 07 08 09 10

SINCERE   01 02 03 04 05 06 07 08 09 10

FORGIVING 01 02 03 04 05 06 07 08 09 10

LOVING   01 02 03 04 05 06 07 08 09 10

CALM   01 02 03 04 05 06 07 08 09 10

have you become more resilient during pregnancy?

NEVER EVER MISTAKE
HER SILENCE FOR
WEAKNESS. REMEMBER
THAT SOMETIMES THE
AIR STILLS, BEFORE
THE ONSET OF A
HURRICANE...

SOCIAL CONNECTION

You are going on a scavenger hunt. It's probably been a while so let's review the rules.
Find the items listed on the right. Describe your experience once you've found all items.

scavenger hunt

SOMEONE HELPING
SOMEONE

A MOTHER TRYING
HER BEST

SOMEONE LOVING
THEIR JOB

A PERSON WHO IS
DEEPLY HAPPY

A KIND SMILE

A CHILD ENJOYING
LIFE

SOMEONE WHO
NEEDS A HUG

AN ANIMAL SLEEPING

A COUPLE IN LOVE

SOMEONE ENJOYING
SOLITUDE

LAUGHTER FROM A
LARGE GROUP

SOMEONE NOT
GLUED TO THEIR
PHONE

SOMEONE
CELEBRATING

SINGING AND
DANCING

POTENTIALLY A FIRST
DATE

SOMEONE YOU WANT
TO KNOW

AGELESS BEAUTY

A DEFINITION OF
LOVE

ALONE CHALLENGE

Indulge in your alone time while you can. Finding the beauty in enjoying activities alone deepens mindfuless. Track how often you do the following:

Walking alone										
Dining alone										
Shopping solo										
Day trip										
_____ (write in your own)										

WHAT DO YOU ENJOY MOST ABOUT BEING ALONE?

ACKNOWLEDGEMENT

be true to yourself

Think of the first response that comes to mind about your mindset while pregnant.

.01   *I am driven by...*

.02   *I will one day...*

.03   *I believe in...*

.04   *I have the goal to...*

.05   *I have the habit of...*

5 LOVE LANGUAGES

Take the 5 Love Languages quiz (www.5lovelanguages.com) to determine what your preference is for giving and receiving love. Once identified, seek to love yourself better by speaking your own love language.

In addition to the examples below, write how you show yourself love.

words of affirmation
- say a confidence mantra
- daily compliment
- speak compassionately to yourself

gifts
- treat yourself to a present
- indulge in your favorite store
- proudly show off your purchase

acts of service
- finish the project you've started
- get ahead of your to-do list
- acknowledge your accomplishments

quality time
- enjoy a movie by yourself
- indulge in a bubble bath
- feel confident in saying no to going out with friends

physical touch
- soak those pregnant feet
- massage your tired hands
- get a massage

MANAGE EXPECTATIONS

Spontaneity is a skill that many people do not possess. As an expectant mother you can plan and plan, and then plan some more, but children don't tend to follow most plans. Developing your ability to roll with the punches and go with the flow will help when your perfectly planned play date gets rained out or your child is sick on vacation. Letting go of expectations helps develop real happiness.

Happiness = Reality - Expectations

The only portion of this equation that you can control is your expectations. Lowering unrealistic standards will help you appreciate things and others for what they are.

What have you planned for recently that your expectations might be too high for? The next time something doesn't go as planned, take a deep breath and see it as an opportunity to learn to be spontaneous. You get extra credit if you do a happy dance at the red light when you are running late. People may think you're crazy (but that's fun, too).

WHEN YOU STEP INTO
YOUR POWER AND YOUR
TRUE AUTHENTIC SELF,
YOU SHINE. YOU SHINE
SO BRIGHTLY THAT THE
WORLD TRIES TO KEEP UP.

———

GRATITUDE

Thank you is a powerful combination of two simple words.

People love receiving thank you letters (pieces of paper that come in the mailbox from the postman, can be rarely found within the junk mail). Although thank you texts and emails are better than nothing at all, consider taking some time to handwrite and mail your next batch of thank you letters.

Treat thanking someone as an opportunity to gift your gratitude with love. This is the occasion to use your fancy pens and beautiful stationery.

When writing your letter, use language that is genuine to you, a formal thank you might not be seen as genuine. Acknowledge specifically what the receiver did that made you feel thankful. Mention how the act of service or gift makes you feel and how you value it.

SAMPLE

Dear Mom,

Thank you for spending the week with Bellamy and me. I appreciate you taking time from your busy schedule to focus on us. We will cherish the great memories from Gatlinburg. As I reflect on the pictures from the trip, I can hear the laughter jumping out and singing in my ears. Please know that I am grateful for everything.

Love,
Elle

those to thank:

GOAL SETTING

Create five goals that you can accomplish before baby comes. Make your goals SMART (Specific, Measurable, Attainable, Relevant and Time-based).

.01

.02

.03

.04

.05

WHO WILL YOU ASK TO HOLD YOU ACCOUNTABLE?

RELATIONSHIPS

identify a healthy relationship

Below are the five components of a healthy relationship. How do you contribute each component to those in your life?

Example: My friends know they can trust me because I rarely cancel and always keep confidentiality.

.01 Accountability;

.02 Trust;

.03 Cooperation;

.04 Support;

.05 Honesty;

FOOD MEDITATION

Eating is a great opportunity to connect to your present moment while nourishing your body. Food meditation is great for beginners, as you have regular opportunities for practice. The next time you sit down to eat, create a calming environment. Remove all electronics and distractions from your reach. Before you take a bite, pay close attention to your food. What colors and shapes do you see? What imperfections make your meal unique? Appreciate where your food came from and the preparation it took. When eating, chew slowly and try to taste every morsel. Breathe in between bites to savor the flavors. What noises do you hear? What textures can you feel? As you focus on your meal, your energy will relax. You may even notice baby enjoying something you're eating with a kick or movement, too.

visioning is a powerful tool. try to envision your baby's birth. what would your ideal birth look, sound, and feel like?

YOU ATTRACT
OTHERS WHEN
YOU HAVE A
SENSE OF WHO
YOU ARE.

CONVERSATIONS

change the conversation

The next five people who text you, respond back
with a call instead of a text. By responding in a more
personalized manner, you'll deepen the relationship and
probably surprise your friend. Write about your comfort
level and response to each call.

KINDNESS
noun

The quality of being friendly, generous and considerate.

synonyms: kindliness, kindheartedness, warmheartedness, affection, warmth, gentleness, concern, care, consideration, helpfulness, thoughtfulness, unselfishness, selflessness, altruism, compassion, sympathy, understanding, big-heartedness, benevolence, benignity, friendliness, hospitality, neighborliness, generosity, magnanimity, and charitableness.

IN WHAT WAYS DO YOU SHOW KINDNESS TO OTHERS?

do you believe that your emotions have changed
with pregancy? do you believe it is good or bad?

BEING THE STUDENT

We often find ourselves feeling as though we are supposed to take on the role of teachers for our children. It can be overwhelming to reflect on the sheer volume of advice, lessons, and stories we want to impart to our children. We hold a lot of weight with this burden.

What if we flipped the lens and reversed roles? What if we thought of ourselves as the student? If we sit in the student's seat, we allow ourselves to permit the child to be who they are and who they were born to be. We allow them to explore the world and make their own stories and beliefs. We then become a sponge of information and new perspectives; we learn. It's almost as though we are the children all over again. We get to experience life without the assumptions and stories that we were told. We become open and eager to allow our children the space to share.

Try to think of the life inside you as someone you need to learn from. What is the baby trying to tell you and show you? How could your pregnancy be different if you allowed the child to be the teacher?

COMPARISON

There are some similarities and some differences
between mindfulness and meditation.

Can you define the difference between mindfulness and
meditation? Do some research and write down what you learn.

How can you better incorporate mindfulness
into your daily routine to help you and baby?

when you are brought
into this life, you're
given certain gifts and
you have to use them

SOCIAL CONNECTION

It's time to dance! Take a lesson. Mimic a YouTube video. Re-enact your middle school talent show. Dance with your baby bump. Dance with friends. Describe your experience:

Types of dance

LATIN

CHA CHA

SALSA

HAND JIVE

CAROLINA SHAG

POLE DANCE

BOOGIE-WOOGIE

BALLROOM

TAP

TANGO

WALTZ

QUICKSTEP

FOXTROT

HIP-HOP

BOUNCE

LINE DANCE

ROBOT

BREAK DANCE

DISCO

SQUARE DANCE

BELLY DANCE

BALLET

COOKING MEDITATION

Doing a cooking meditation will teach you to relax and be present while cooking, and also leaves you with a delicious meal made with love. Does mixing meditation with cooking seem crazy? Well, it's easier than you'd think. To cook mindfully, remember to slow down everything that you do. Start by carefully reading your recipe. Be present with each step. As you begin by gathering ingredients, become mindful of your kitchen.

> What does the kitchen feel like?
> What does the lighting do for you?
> How is the temperature?
> What do you enjoy most about your kitchen?

Once you begin your recipe, follow each step as though you are in slow motion.

> Cut your vegetables with precision and grace.
> Smell your ingredients.
> Embrace the texture of your food.
> Pay close attention to the transformation of your food from raw to cooked.

Throughout your cooking, pay attention to your thoughts. If your mind wanders off your cooking and to your to-do list, kindly bring your attention and focus back to cooking.

GRATEFUL DAYS

In the box, tally each time you successfully accomplished the task.

Write in your gratitude journal									
Call a family member									
Spend time with kids									
Volunteer to help someone									
Cook with love									

REFLECTIONS

GRATEFUL IN 3'S

challenge
Write three things you are grateful for in each category.

bonus
Include why each of the three things makes your grateful.

THINGS I HEAR

THINGS IN MY HOME

PEOPLE THAT I WORK WITH

ANIMALS IN MY LIFE

TEACHERS

COMFORT ZONES

Think of five seperate times you've stretched beyond your comfort zone.

.01

.02

.03

.04

.05

DO YOU SEE ANY PATTERNS OF GROWTH WHEN STRETCHED OUTSIDE YOUR COMFORT ZONE?

We should always have
THREE friends in our lives:

ONE who walks ahead, who
we look up to and follow;

ONE who walks beside us,
who is with us every step of
the journey;

and then, **ONE** who we reach
back for and bring along
after we've cleared the way.

ACKNOWLEDGEMENTS

I am blessed to have so many wonderful people who helped me convert my idea into reality. Thank you for your support, talent, nurturing and patience.

SARA ALSOBROOKS

SAM AMICK

KIMBERLY BELLANTI-BARTHO

BELLAMY BENSON

BRYAN BENSON

SUE AND TOM BENSON

ALI BREWER

ALEX BROWNFIELD

CLOUD FAMILY

CHRIS CROUCH

DERRICK FURLOW

EMILY CULLUM

ELLIS FAMILY

LISA ENGELKING

RACHEL DELLINGER

KELLIE DOYLE

MALIA HUTCHISON

LARRY KRIGER

GOLDIE LITTLEJOHN

TRISH LOCKARD

DEBBIE L. LONDON

TIFFANI MENSCH

SHELBY OOTEN

MICHELLE RODEMS

JUDITH ROSENBERG

JOHN SEPICH

BROOKE STANFILL

TEAM AT THE ALLIANCE FOR BETTER NONPROFITS

KATE TURNBULL

COLLEEN AND JOE WHEELER

AUDREY VESTAL

VINEA MENTORS

Cheers,

ELLE BENSON

Brown, Brené. Rising Strong. First edition. New York: Spiegel & Grau, an imprint of Random House, 2015.

Cain, Susan. Quiet. Crown, 2012.

Carson, Rachel. The Sense of Wonder. Harper & Row, 1965.

Chodron, Pema. When Things Fall Apart: Heart Advice for Difficult Times. Shambhala Publications, 2002, 58.

Cuddy, Amy. "Your Body Language May Shape Who You Are." TED Talks, https://www.ted.com/talks/amy_cuddy_your_body_language_shapes_who_you_are. Accessed 26 Apr. 2019.

Firestone, Lisa. "Benefits of Mindfulness." Psychology Today, 6 Mar. 2013, http://www.psychologytoday.com/blog/compassion-matters/201303/benefits-mindfulness.

Gielan, Michelle. Broadcasting Happinesss. BenBella Books, Inc. 2015.

Gordon, C. L., Arnette, R. A., & Smith, R. E. (2011). Have you thanked your spouse today?: Felt and expressed gratitude among married couples. Personality and Individual Differences, 50(3), 339-343.

Greater Good Science Center at UC Berkeley. Official Web site. https://greatergood.berkeley.edu/

Harris, Dan. 10% Happier: How I Tamed the Voice in My Head, Reduced Stress Without Losing My Edge, and Found Self-help That Actually Works--a True Story. New York: It Books, 2014.

Haslet, Adrianne. www.adriannehaslet.com
H, H. "How to Be Happy." Happier Human, 4 Jan. 2019, https://www.happierhuman.com/benefits-of-gratitude/.

"How to Stop Negative Self-Talk." Mayo Clinic, 18 Feb. 2017, https://www.mayoclinic.org/healthy-lifestyle/stress-management/in-depth/positive-thinking/art-20043950.

Huffington, Arianna. Thrive. Harmony, 2014.

Lee, Ingrid Fetell. Joyful: The Surprising Power of Ordinary Things to Create Extraordinary Happiness. Rider, 2019.

Lyubomirsky, Sonja. The Myths of Happiness. New York, Penguin Books, 2014.

Malchiodi, Cathy. "Creativity as a Wellness Practice." Psychology Today, 31 Dec. 2015, https://www.psychologytoday.com/blog/arts-and-health/201512/creativity-wellness-practice.

McArthur, Ellen. "The Surprising Thing I Learned Sailing Solo Around the World." TED2015, March 2015. www.ted.com/talks

Mitchell, Maria. Maria Mitchell: Life, Letters and Journals. Ed. Phebe Mitchell Kendall. Lee and Shepard, 1896.

Moody, L. (2019). The Five Love Languages Defined - The 5 Love Languages®. [online] The 5 Love Languages®. Available at: https://www.5lovelanguages.com/2018/06/the-five-love-languages-defined/ [Accessed 29 Apr. 2019].

[online] Self-Esteem Journal. Available at: https://www.therapistaid.com/therapy-worksheet/self-esteem-journal/self-esteem/adults [Access 16, May 2019].

Moralis, Shonda. Breathe, Mama Breathe. New York: Experiment, 2017.

Park, N., & Peterson, C. (2009). Character strengths: Research and practice. Journal of college and character, 10(4).

Poehler, Amy. Yes Please. Dey Street, 2014.

Puddicombe, Andy. The Headspace Guide to a Mindful Pregnancy. London, Hodder & Stoughton. 2017.

Ricard, Matthieu. Happiness. Little, Brown, 2008.
Rowling, J. K. Very Good Lives. Little, Brown and Company, 2015.

Seligman, M. E., Steen, T. A., Park, N., & Peterson, C. (2005). Positive psychology progress: empirical validation of interventions. American psychologist, 60(5), 410.

Sinek, Simon. Leaders Eat Last: Why Some Teams Pull Together and Others Don't. New York: Portfolio/Penguin, 2014.

Tolle, Eckhart. The Power of Now: A Guide to Spiritual Enlightenment. Vancouver : Novato, Calif.: Namaste Pub., 2004.

Yousafzai, Malala. "Address on Malala Day." The United Nations Youth Assembly, New York, July 12 2013. www.youtube.com/watch?v=3rNhZu3ttlU.

Author Bio

Elle Benson is what many would describe as a typical working mother. She's the one on mute during the conference call, balancing her phone on one shoulder and her toddler in the other arm. One minute she's researching toddler books starring powerful females, and the next minute she's helping nonprofit organization build the capacity to achieve their missions. She doesn't believe there's a science to motherhood, but does believe that women need to stop judging others, and, more importantly, themselves. She began studying positive psychology to help people finish the phrase, "I'll be happy when…" Her desire is to assist others with being happy in the present moment. and equip nonprofits to better serve their communities.

Education

MBA in Organizational Leadership, University of Tiffin, 2015
BS in Business, University of Tennessee, 2007

Additional

Certificate in Science of Happiness, University of California Berkeley, 2015
Board Member, Association of Infant Mental Health in Tennessee, 2017 - Current
Board Member, Friends of Literacy, 2015 - Current
Member, Knoxville Writers Guild, 2016 - Current

CULTIVATEYOURHAPPINESS.CO

Made in the USA
Lexington, KY
24 August 2019